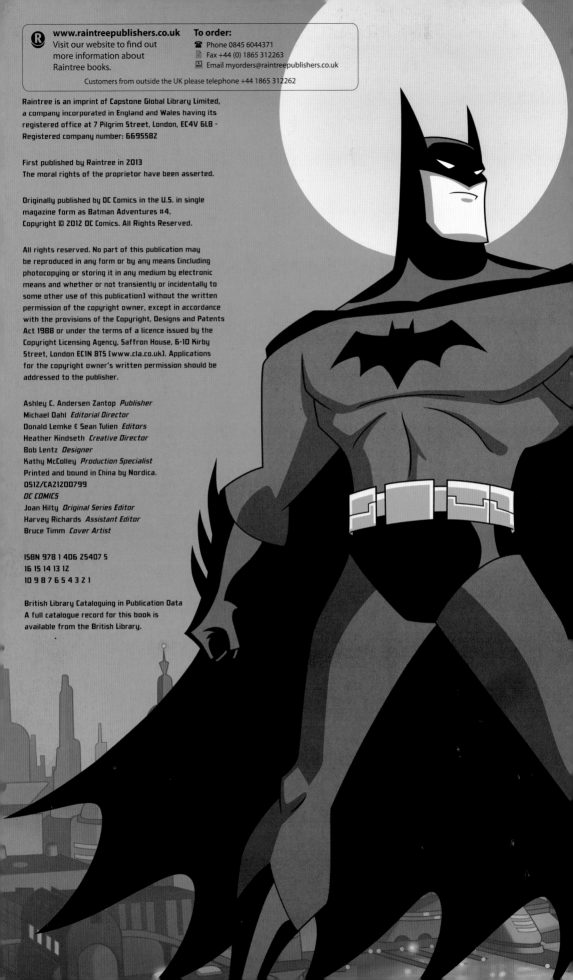

**R** **www.raintreepublishers.co.uk**
Visit our website to find out
more information about
Raintree books.

**To order:**
☎ Phone 0845 6044371
📠 Fax +44 (0) 1865 312263
✉ Email myorders@raintreepublishers.co.uk

Customers from outside the UK please telephone +44 1865 312262

Raintree is an imprint of Capstone Global Library Limited,
a company incorporated in England and Wales having its
registered office at 7 Pilgrim Street, London, EC4V 6LB -
Registered company number: 6695582

First published by Raintree in 2013
The moral rights of the proprietor have been asserted.

Originally published by DC Comics in the U.S. in single
magazine form as Batman Adventures #4.
Copyright © 2012 DC Comics. All Rights Reserved.

Ashley C. Andersen Zantop *Publisher*
Michael Dahl *Editorial Director*
Donald Lemke & Sean Tulien *Editors*
Heather Kindseth *Creative Director*
Bob Lentz *Designer*
Kathy McColley *Production Specialist*
Printed and bound in China by Nordica.
0512/CA21200799
*DC COMICS*
Joan Hilty *Original Series Editor*
Harvey Richards *Assistant Editor*
Bruce Timm *Cover Artist*

ISBN 978 1 406 25407 5
16 15 14 13 12
10 9 8 7 6 5 4 3 2 1

British Library Cataloguing in Publication Data
A full catalogue record for this book is
available from the British Library.

# BATMAN ADVENTURES

## NEED TO KNOW

Ty Templeton & Dan Slott......................writers
Rick Burchett & Ty Templeton .......... pencillers
Terry Beatty ................................................ inker
Lee Loughridge & Zylonol Studios .......colorists
Phil Felix ...................................................letterer

Batman created by
Bob Kane

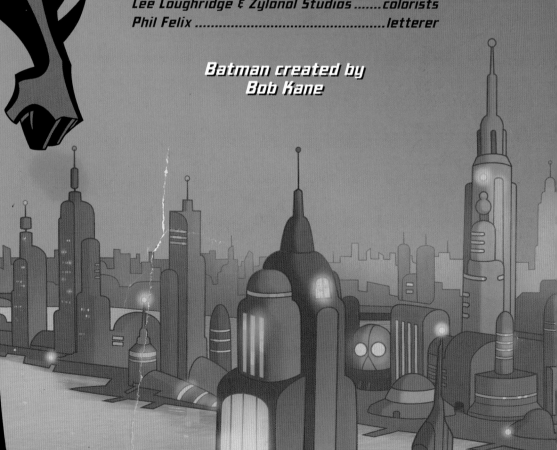

**DING DONG!**

HEY, ALF! TELL BRUCE I'M READY.

READY, MS. MADISON...?

AH, YES. READY FOR YOUR *DATE*, THIS EVENING.

DANCING AT THE X-RAY TERRACE, IF I RECALL.

UH-OH, I KNOW *THAT* LOOK.

HE'S *FORGOTTEN*, HASN'T HE?

BUT I'M AFRAID MASTER BRUCE *HAS* BEEN CALLED AWAY... ON *EX-TREMELY* IMPORTANT BUSINESS.

I AM TO CONVEY HIS *DEEP REGRETS*.

NOT AT ALL.

*WHY* DOES HE KEEP *DOING* THIS?

WHAT'S MORE IMPORTANT THAN *ME*?

# THE BALANCE

TY TEMPLETON ———— WRITER
RICK BURCHETT ———— PENCILLER
TERRY BEATTY ———— INKER
LEE LOUGHRIDGE ———— COLORIST
PHIL FELIX ———— LETTERER
HARVEY RICHARDS ——— ASSISTANT
JOAN HILTY ———— EDITOR
BATMAN CREATED BY *BOB KANE*

SO, WHAT'S UNDER THE CREEPY GIANT HEAD?

ARE WE TALKING SECRET HIDEOUT, OR MOLDY MUSEUM STUFF?

IT'S VENTILATED... THERE'S A STRONG BREEZE.

...AND A SLIGHT *GLOW* TO THE SOUTH OF THIS AREA.

I'M IN A CHAMBER CARVED FROM THE VOLCANIC ROCK. HARD TO GUESS THE AGE...

MAYBE *CENTURIES.*

HIS TRAINING CAMP IN MANGAREVA WAS BUILT ON THE NEAREST INHABITABLE LAND TO *EASTER ISLAND.*

RA'S OBSESSION WITH ANCIENT MYSTICISM AND THE SYMBOLS OF RESURRECTION MAKES IT IMPOSSIBLE TO PASS THAT OFF AS *COINCIDENCE.*

SINCE HE WASN'T AT THE CAMP... HE'S GOT TO BE *HERE.*

IT COULD BE DESERTED.

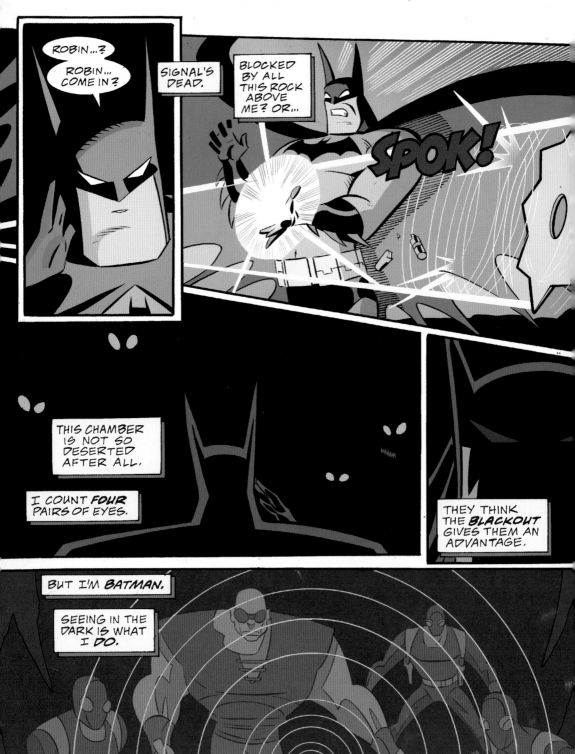

ROBIN...?
ROBIN... COME IN?

SIGNAL'S DEAD.

BLOCKED BY ALL THIS ROCK ABOVE ME? OR...

SPOK!

THIS CHAMBER IS NOT SO DESERTED AFTER ALL.

I COUNT *FOUR* PAIRS OF EYES.

THEY THINK THE *BLACKOUT* GIVES THEM AN ADVANTAGE.

BUT I'M *BATMAN.*

SEEING IN THE DARK IS WHAT I *DO.*

SOMEONE *ELSE* IN THE ROOM.

*PERFUME* ON THE BREEZE,,,

...*ROSES*?

GGKK!

Hwk!

*TALIA.*

≋SIGH!≋ YOU AND MY *FATHER.*

WHAT AM I GOING TO *DO* WITH YOU?

THE UNMISTAKABLE SMELL OF ROTTING MEAT AND JASMINE WAKES ME.

ONE OF THE MYSTERIOUS **HEALING POOLS** IN WHICH RA'S AL GHUL IMMERSES HIMSELF IN ORDER TO REMAIN **IMMORTAL**.

THESE PITS HAVE KEPT HIM ALIVE FOR **CENTURIES**—BUT THEY LONG AGO DROVE HIM **MAD**.

I'M NEAR A **LAZARUS PIT**.

RAPA NUI IS **SACRED** TO ME, DETECTIVE.

I'VE RETURNED HERE **OFTEN** SINCE MY YEARS WITH **CAPTAIN COOK** AND THE **BRITISH NAVY**...

THIS TRAGIC ISLAND IS NEVER FAR FROM MY THOUGHTS.

BUT WHY ARE **YOU** HERE? WHY **NOW**?

BECAUSE YOU WEREN'T AT YOUR BASE ON MANGA-REVA.

I'M **AMAZED** YOU DISCOVERED THAT INSTALLATION. NO DOUBT THAT'S WHY WE **LOST** CONTACT WITH THEM...

YOU SENT **SHADOW ASSASSINS** FROM THERE TO GOTHAM. TRIED TO KILL **JOKER, TWO-FACE, POISON IVY, RIDDLER**...

WHY?

ARE YOU MOVING INTO GOTHAM AND ELIMINATING THE **COMPETITION**?

NO.

SETTLING A **VENDETTA**?

NO.

NO VENDETTAS. IT WAS A *GIFT*.

MURDER...

...IS A *GIFT*?

OF PEOPLE SUCH AS YOU MENTIONED...? *ABSOLUTELY.*

FOR YOU.

I'M *CENTURIES OLD,* DETECTIVE, AND I SUPPOSE SOMEWHAT *SENTIMENTAL.*

AS MUCH TIME AS I DEVOTE TO RESCUING HIS POOR, BELEAGUERED PLANET FROM THE *DEATH GRIP* HUMANITY HAS UPON IT...

...I SPEND AN EQUAL AMOUNT OF TIME CONSIDERING MY *DAUGHTER.*

YOU'RE VERY *IMPORTANT* TO HER, SHE SEES *GREATNESS* IN YOU.

SOMETIMES I WONDER IF IT'S NOT ALL JUST TO *IRRITATE* HER FATHER...

BUT WHERE SHE SEES *GREATNESS,* I SEE A *GREAT* MANY *DISTRACTIONS,*

SO I CHOSE TO *REMOVE* THEM FOR YOU, AS A GESTURE OF *GOODWILL* BETWEEN US. SIMPLY THAT.

CALL IT OFF!

NO ONE DIES FOR ME!

COME NOW, BRUCE. YOU'VE NEVER *WISHED* THEM DEAD...EVEN FOR JUST A *MOMENT*?

MY FATHER OFFERS TO SOLVE *ALL* YOUR PROBLEMS...

...AND YOU GET TO KEEP THE *BLOOD* AWAY FROM YOUR HANDS.

YOU AND I CAN FINALLY FIND THE TIME TO--

TALIA... YOU'RE AS *SICK* AS HE IS.

BELOVED...? YOU'RE *ABLE TO STAND?* THE POTION IN THAT DART--

...WAS AN *OLD* FORMULA I'D FOUND AN ANTI-TOXIN FOR *MONTHS* AGO.

RA'S-- --I'VE *HAD* IT WITH *YOU* PLAYING GOD!

WHAT...?

POW!

YOU **STRUCK** ME?

TO WHAT END? YOU'RE OUTNUMBERED, OUTGUNNED...

BECAUSE YOU'RE COMING **BACK** WITH ME THIS TIME.

YOU'RE GOING TO **PAY** FOR YOUR CRIMES, ONCE AND FOR ALL!

PREPOSTEROUS.

UBU-- KILL HIM SWIFTLY.

COME, DAUGHTER-- YOU SHOULDN'T SEE THIS.

NO!

THUK!

THUK!

THUK!

BE... BELOVED...? I...

TALIA!

NO...

UHHH...

WE SHOT THE DAUGHTER.

WE WERE ORDERED TO FIRE.

WILL IT MATTER?

RA'S WILL KILL US ALL!

STOP! IT IS YOUR DUTY TO DIE FOR THE MASTER COWARDS!

YOU STAY AND DO YOUR DUTY, THEN!

THERE'S STILL A CHANCE!

SHE'S FALLEN INTO THE LAZARUS PIT--ITS HEALING POWERS SHOULD SAVE HER!

IF SHE IS STRONG ENOUGH TO SURVIVE THE BLOOD MADNESS THAT FOLLOWS...

DAUGHTER...?

82

GRAAAAH!

MY LEGS GIVE OUT FOR A SECOND.

I HOPE RA'S IS IN WORSE SHAPE.

CAN YOU MOVE?

BARELY...

YOU DIDN'T FIGHT BACK.

SHE IS MY *DAUGHTER.*

I COULD NO MORE RAISE MY HAND TO HARM HER...

...THAN *YOU* COULD.

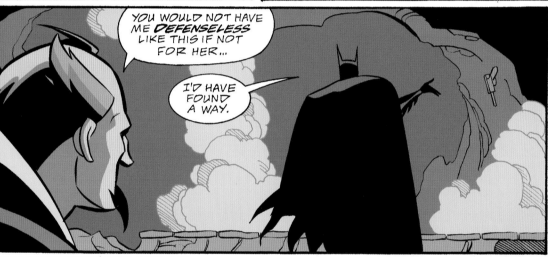

YOU WOULD NOT HAVE ME *DEFENSELESS* LIKE THIS IF NOT FOR HER...

I'D HAVE FOUND A WAY.

BUT TO DO *THIS.*

TO USE HER SHAMEFUL MOMENT OF MADNESS TO *YOUR* ADVANTAGE IN THIS *GAME* WE PLAY...

SHE WON'T FORGIVE IT.

MURDER IS *NOT A GAME,* RA'S --

--AND YOU'RE *NOT* ESCAPING JUSTICE ANY-MORE.

MMM...

I DO NOT KNOW. I AWOKE ONLY MOMENTS BEFORE YOU.

UBU?

WHERE IS MY FATHER?

HE DETECTIVE IS GONE ALSO.

WE SHOULD BE MOVING FROM HERE...

THE THICK SMOKE FROM THIS *MOAI* WILL BRING PEOPLE TO INVESTIGATE.

IS THERE A MESSAGE FOR ME? FROM--

NO MESSAGE.

NO MESSAGE...?

WHY WOULD HE *DO* THAT TO ME?

NEXT ISSUE:

DEADSHOT!

# CREATORS

### TY TEMPLETON WRITER & PENCILLER

Ty Templeton was born in the wilds of downtown Toronto, Canada to a show-business family. He makes his living writing and drawing comic books, working on such characters as Batman, Superman, Spider-Man, The Simpsons, the Avengers, and many others.

### DAN SLOTT WRITER

Dan Slott is a comics writer best known for his work on DC Comics' *Arkham Asylum*, and, for Marvel, *The Avengers* and the *Amazing Spider-Man*.

### RICK BURCHETT PENCILLER

Rick Burchett has worked as a comics artist for more than 25 years. He has received the comics industry's Eisner Award three times, Spain's Haxtur Award, and he has been nominated for the Eagle Award. Rick lives with his wife and two sons in Missouri, USA.

### TERRY BEATTY INKER

For more than ten years, Terry Beatty was the main inker of DC Comics' "animated-style" Batman comics, including *The Batman Strikes*. More recently, he worked on *Return to Perdition*, a graphic novel for DC's Vertigo Crime.

# GLOSSARY

*analysis* examination of a whole to discover its elements and their relations

*assassin* person who kills another person, often for money

*beleaguered* subject to troublesome force

*disciplines* areas of study

*engage* enter into contest or battle with

*foe* enemy, or one who hates another

*immortal* living or lasting forever

*magnify* enlarge or make bigger

*microorganism* organism (as a bacterium) of microscopic or less than microscopic size

*mite* tiny animal with eight legs that is related to a spider

*mysticism* experience of mystical union or direct communication with a spirit

*preposterous* ridiculous or absurd

*resurrection* rising again to life

*vendetta* series of acts marked by bitter hostility and motivated by a desire for revenge

# BATMAN GLOSSARY

**Alfred Pennyworth:** Bruce Wayne's loyal butler. He knows Bruce Wayne's secret identity and helps the Dark Knight solve crimes in Gotham City.

**Batgirl:** one of the Dark Knight's crime-fighting partners, secretly Commissioner Gordon's daughter Barbara.

**Ra's al Ghul:** a centuries-old villain who hopes to save the world by killing most of humanity and ruling the few people who remain.

**Robin:** one of the Dark Knight's crime-fighting partners, secretly Bruce Wayne's ward Dick Grayson.

**Society of Shadows:** an organization of highly trained assassins led by Ra's al Ghul.

**Talia al Ghul:** the daughter of Ra's al Ghul and a member of the Society of Shadows.

# VISUAL QUESTIONS & PROMPTS

**1.** The Dark Knight is an expert martial artist. Find at least two panels in this book where Batman uses this skill. Do you believe he could've solved those problems differently? Explain your answer.

**2.** Batman has many crime-fighting skills, including the ability to see in the dark. What are some other skills that the Dark Knight has? Find panels in this book where he uses those or other abilities.

**3.** In comic books, sound effects (also known as SFX) are used to show sounds, such as the firing of a gun or other weapon. Make a list of all the sound effects in this book, and then write a definition for each term. Soon, you'll have your own SFX dictionary!

**4.** Comic book illustrators draw motion lines (also known as action lines) to show movement of a character or an object, like Talia's fist in the panel below. Find other panels in this book with motion lines. Do you think they make the illustrations more exciting? Why or why not?

**5.** The Dark Knight doesn't use guns to fight crime. Why do you think he chooses not to carry this type of weapon? Do you think this puts the super hero at a disadvantage? Why or why not?

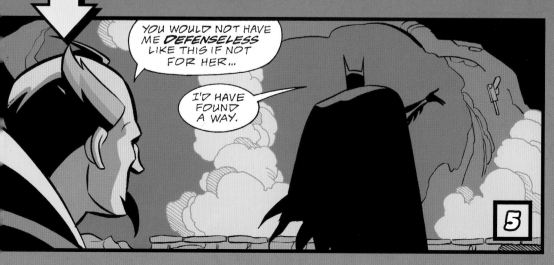

# BATMAN
## ADVENTURES

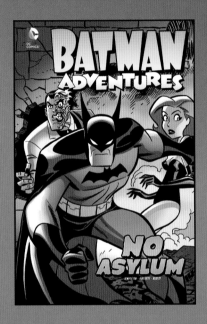

Raintree